AMAZONIA
where tree
frogs go moo!

AIRMAIL FROM...

AMAZONIA-
where tree frogs go moo!

Michael Cox

Illustrated by
Rhian Nest James

Hippo

Scholastic Children's Books,
Commonwealth House, 1-19 New Oxford Street
London WC1A 1NU, UK

A division of Scholastic Ltd
London ~ New York ~ Toronto ~ Sydney ~ Auckland
Mexico City ~ New Delhi ~ Hong Kong

Published in the UK by Scholastic Ltd, 1999

Text copyright © Michael Cox, 1999
Illustrations copyright © Rhian Nest James, 1999

ISBN 0 439 01073 X

All rights reserved
Typeset by M Rules
Printed by Cox & Wyman Ltd, Reading, Berks

2 4 6 8 10 9 5 3 1

The right of Michael Cox and Rhian Nest James to be identified as
the author and illustrator of this work respectively has been asserted by
them in accordance with the Copyright, Designs and Patents Act, 1988.

Amazonia – where tree frogs go moo! is part of a series of books about fascinating countries around the world. Each book is made up of letters written by a boy or girl who lives in one of these countries. You might find that their English isn't always quite right (unlike yours, which is always perfect - ha ha!). So watch out for a few mistakes and crossings out. Sometimes in their letters the children use words from their own language (just like we all do!).

Some words in Brazilian Portuguese are quite similar to the English ones that mean the same thing. Try this one for starters! "Excelente". Yes . . . it means "Excellent"! See, you've already learned your first bit of Brazilian Portuguese! Where the words are a bit harder their English meaning comes after them in brackets. But being so 'brilhante', you've probably worked that out for yourself already!

10 Janeiro (January)

Hi to you!

How are you? My name is Maria Lisboa and I live in Copacabana which is in the marvellous city of Rio de Janeiro in Brazil. Look! Can you see me on this map?

EQUATOR

AMAZON

River Amazon

BASIN

BRASILIA

This is my map of BRAZIL

Atlantic Ocean

● Rio de Janeiro

↑ (I am here in-)
COPACABANA

I am nearly ten years old and a girl. Me and my twin brother, Leonardo, live in an apartment inside a great big tall skyscraper with our mum, Gabriela, and our dad, Fernando.

our apartment – it's high, isn't it?

In just a few months' time me and Leo are going on a very big holiday with our Uncle Jesus. Guess where he is taking us? Amazonia! To the Amazon rainforest! For nearly three whole weeks! Yes! It will

Uncle Jesus

be the adventure trip of our lifetime! Aren't we lucky? Our brilliant Uncle says there are lots of kids who will probably never get to go on a trip like this and it would be good for us to share our excitements and explorings with someone else.

So that is why we have decided to write to you – to tell you all about our adventures as they happen! But before that, if you don't mind, we would also like to be your normal pen-pals for a while, and keep you up-to-date on some other things about our life. We have got tons to tell you! Our letters will soon be flying to your front door fast and thick!

Just the other side of my bedroom wall right now I can hear Leo pounding his big

Leo's samba drum

samba drum to a pop band on his fi-hi. He should be writing to you but he has got a bit carried away and is pretending to be a drumming star . . . one of his favourite things! I will go next door right now and get him busy with his pen and paper!

I'll write you again real soon.

Your brand new pen-friend,

Maria

PS If it seems like Leo is showing off - take no notice! He's got a big opinion of himself. But he's Ok really. Yes I am! L.

10 Janeiro

Oi!

It's me, the Copacabana Kid! How you doing? Tudo bem? (Everything OK?) My twin sister has just been to my room. She has told me to get writing to you. So now my pen is just screeeeching across this piece of paper!

Now . . . listen to this! The first things I would like to tell you about are my great futebol (football) skills. They are tremendously remarkable. You should see my:

back-of-the-heels flick...

banana kick

... and my over-the-head backward bicycle kick.

They are out of this world! All the kids in my

school cry "Brilhante Leo!" (Cool Leo!) when I do my soccer tricks. They think I am the business. They're right! Don't be sad that you can't see me do my stuff for real. One day I'll be doing it on your TV screen. When I am playing for Brazil in the World Cup. Yesss!

My other big thrill thing is music. All kinds. Pop . . . jazz . . . roll and rock . . . and of course, Brazilian samba! I think they are all cool. I will probably have my own rock band when I am about 30 and have finished being a top football dude.

↑ Stop talking about yourself Leo! M.

OK, OK, so . . . now to my folks. Dad is a car dealer. He sells Mercedes to rich people. He is car mad and talks cars, cars, cars, all the time. On the next page is my brilhante picture of him:

my dad →

Mum works for a TV company. She is also a big cooker. She makes great moqueca (shrimp stew) and lots of other tasty stuff for us. She is cool!

← Mum at the TV studio

OK! That's it for now. I got to go meet my pals for a futebol training session and some "batendo um papo", which means have a chat, mess about, that sort of thing! I'll just take this letter to Maria to check it out. She thinks she is cleverest because she is oldest. But only by ten minutes! I don't think it makes that much difference! Do you? Stay cool!

Your brand new pen,

Leo

14 Janeiro

Dear friend,

Bom dia! (Good morning!) It's me, Maria. How are you? I hope my twin brother's letter was not too shocking for you? Sometimes I think he is "um pouco louco" (slightly crazy!)! *Take no notice - this is just her joke. L.*

Now - I must tell you what my favourite spare time things are! First I like to dance, especially the samba. I do that with our "samba escola" (samba school). They are a big team of people from around here who all do dancing together. I'm in the children's section and Leo's in the "samba bateria". That's the drummer squad who make the music for us. In just a few weeks' time we are going to take part in the samba dancing parades at Rio's fantastic Carnival.

SAMBA
SAMBA
SAMBA!

13

Have you heard of our world famous street party? It is completely estupendo (wonderful!)!

My other favourite spare time activity is wildlifes! Do you like Nature things? I'm entirely mad on them! I love reading and writing about them and I adore to make drawings of them. Our great jungle trip will be just perfect for me. When I am bigger I am going to be a special worker who protects nature from destruction and pollution . . . maybe I will even be an insect man . . . just like Uncle Jesus!

OK! Now to what is happening here at the moment. Today at our school (the normal one – not samba!) we told our teacher about our letters to you. Leo and me are in the same class. Our teacher's name is Mr Silva. He is quite strict but he is very kind. He is also very tall. All the kids call him Mr Anaconda . . . after the giant South American snake. But only when he's not there! Sometimes Leo gets into trouble with Mr Anaconda. Today Mr Anaconda has given him extra homework to make up for the time he has wasted in class. He says Leo should do some writing for you all about Brazil. So, guess what your next letter is going to be about! Hmmm . . . I hope you enjoy it!

It will be magnifico! L.

Ok! Now it's time for me to go do my homework.

Tchau (Goodbye) and all the really best wishes,

Maria

PS What's your teacher like? Do they make you do a stack of homework too?

17 Janeiro

Oi . . . pen!

Hi pal . . . it's me, Leo! How do you ~~went~~ go?
   And what do you know about my country? Any
things . . . or no things? After you read this you will
know lots! Real fast! So here is the big lowdown on
us. Get your head full of it . . . now!

BRAZIL (IN A NUTS - FOR YOU! - BY ME, LEO LISBOA

OUR WEATHER – Tropical. Hot nearly most of the
time. In the far south we have it a bit colder.
NUMBER OF PEOPLE – We have got about 155
million people – nearly three times more than in the
UK. Two out of every three people live in our cities.
That means there is stacks of room left in the rest
of Brazil.
There are some really great football teams from this
continent. Guess who has got the best one! Yesss,
us – BRAZIL! We are the best in the World!
GOOLAAA!

<u>OUR POSITION</u> – We are part of the continent of South America. We take up nearly half of its space:

VENEZUELA
GUYANA
SURINAM
FRENCH GUIANA
ECUADOR
COLOMBIA
PERU
BRAZIL
BOLIVIA
ARGENTINA
PARAGUAY
URUGUAY
CHILE
Pacific Ocean
Atlantic Ocean

<u>LANGUAGE</u> – We speak Brazilian Portuguese. It is like Portuguese Portuguese, but a bit different. Portuguese language was brought to here a long time ago by settler people from Portugal but it has got slightly changed by all the other sorts of people we have got. Maria will tell you some more about this soon.

Oh, thanks for letting me know! M. ➚

OUR SIZE- See how massive Brazil is on the map

Brasil → below? We are the fifth biggest country in the world. Bigger than all the Europe ones put together. 35 times bigger than the UK!

← UK

OUR NEIGHBOURS – We are so big that we have got borders with ten of the 12 other South American countries. All except Ecuador and Chile.

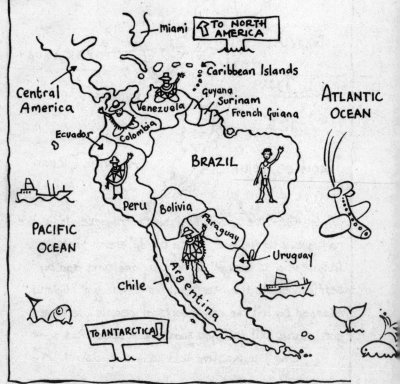

Miami

TO NORTH AMERICA

Caribbean Islands

Central America

Venezuela
Guyana
Surinam
French Guiana

ATLANTIC OCEAN

Ecuador
Colombia

BRAZIL

PACIFIC OCEAN

Peru
Bolivia
Paraguay

Uruguay

Chile

Argentina

TO ANTARCTICA

SOUTH AMERICA - Look at our continent on the map I did for you below. Now look at the African continent. About 150 million years ago they used to be joined together but then they slowly split apart and the Atlantic Ocean filled the space between. Can you see how the edges would still fit together like jigsaw bits if you pushed them back again?

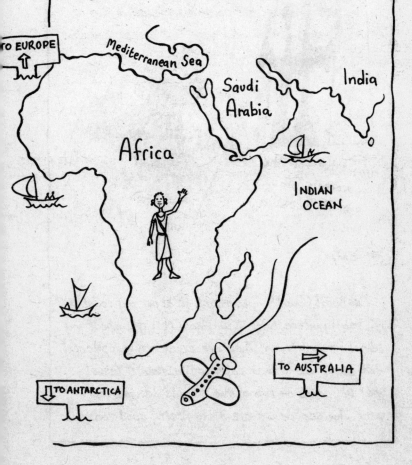

<u>OUR CAPITAL CITY</u> - Brasilia. Until 1960 it was Rio de Janeiro but the government wanted people to go and live in our big empty spaces. So they built this new capital slop bang in the middle of the wildness. Before Rio, Sao Paulo was our capital. But Rio has still got the best futebol stadium! Yesss!

Brasilia's Cathedral

Statue for the workers who built Brasilia.

THE END

OK Bom! (Good!) - so that's it about my country. All really interesting! I will now tell you about my school futebol team! They are excelente (excellent)! And guess who is their capitao (captain)? Yesss! me! We came on top of the schools' league last year. This season we are doing pretty good too.

This is Aldo! →

Except that our goalkeeper, Aldo (my best pal), moved to another escola in Brasilia. His dad and mum have gone there to work. It is terrible. He was really tall with hands like a tree frog's. They stuck on to everything! Nothing got past him. I don't know what we'll do without him. Gotta go now. Time for futebol on TV!

Best wishes,

Leo

Aldo →

← Capitao Leo

24 Janeiro

Dear pen-friend,

Hi there. Now . . . at last you can see a
photo of all my family! I am sorry I did not
send this picture sooner. Our maquina foto
 (camera) got stolen at the beach
and we have only just got the new
one. I hope you like this fotografia
(photograph). Dad took it with our new camera
(set on automatico). We are outside our
apartment block. Yes, that is our car. Dad
thinks it is family. He is proud to pieces of it.

Have you spotted me and Leo are not at all lookalike twins? We are quite different in lots of ways. ← *I am the bonito (handsome) one! L*

Altogether our family has quite a mixture of looks. It is the same in many places in Brazil. If you look at people on the beaches and streets you will see that they are all shapes,

sizes and colours with all sorts of face styles and hair-dos. Our family have all got mainly light brown skin, but me and Dad have got straight black hair and mum has got dark gold and wavy. Leo has just got an enormous dark brown bush on his head. Yes, it is his hair! Curly isn't it? *You are jealous! L.* ↗

All these different looks are because people have come to Brazil from all over the world and through the years they have got all mixed up. To start with there were just South American Indians living here but about 500 years ago settlers from Portugal began arriving.

This is my picture of it!

They claimed the land for themselves and took things from it to send back to Portugal. This was hard work so they made the Indians be their slaves to help them. Which didn't turn out too well. The Indians kept being given diseases by the settlers and dying. Lots of other ones ran away and hid in the forest. Do you blame them? So the Portuguese got millions of new slaves from Africa, who were mainly black.

24

After a bit longer some of the Portuguese people began to marry Indian people and have families. Some Indian people began to marry African people and African people also got married to Portuguese people.

The children from all these families were a real mix-up of colours and sorts. As well, people started coming here from other countries like Russia, Arabia, Germany, Italy and Japan (there are one million from Japan!) and lots, lots more places.

So! Next time you see a picture of our Brazil football team or a film of Carnival you will know why there is such a mixture of colours and faces!

Mum says that our long time back relatives were probably African, Portuguese and Indian. And that is why we look the way we do! I don't think it explains Leo being so crazy though! *Ho, very funny! L.*

I've got to stop now - Daniela, my best friend has just got here. We are going to samba escola (school) to do dancing practice. We cannot miss it. Carnival is only three weeks away. All the samba schools will try to win first prize for best singing and dancing.

Best swishes,

Maria

Me

Daniela

28 Janeiro

Dear new pen-pal,

Bom dia from him. And good day from her. Sim! (Yes!) Today it is a letter from both of your new twin friends. We are typing it. On our dad's old typewriter. Tudo bem? (Everything OK?) We are full of beans. Sim! It is the weekend! Soon we will be having fun. Because we are Cariocas. That's the word for all us people who live in Rio. We are mad on having great times.

So! What's it like where you live? Exciting? Boring? Or just medium? Our city, Rio de Janeiro is amazing. We have got everything! The great big sparkly blue ocean right splash bang in front of us.

Hot blue skys over the top of us!

27

Tall tall sky scrapers, shops, palm trees, restaurants and highways all around us!

And enormous beautiful mountains with wild jungles stuck on our behinds.

It is all excelente (excellent)!

And we have also got the biggest futebol stadium in the whole world! Sim, Rio is a terrific and exciting city to live in. People say there is no other like it anywhere. The eight million of us who live here call it the Cidade Maravilhosa . . . the Marvellous City.

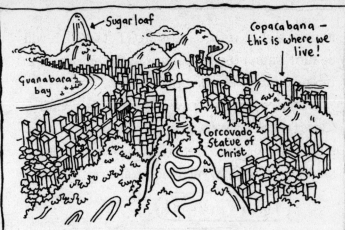

At our part, Copacabana, we have got lovely Copacabana Beach. Have you heard of it? It's a beautiful curving shape with lots of lovely white sand. And really long, about 4.5 kilometres. It takes nearly one hour to walk. Best of all, it's right outside our front door. We want to feel hot sand inside our toes? No problem! We cross the road. We want new sea? Still no problem! There's lots more great beaches really close by.

Does your weather get very warm? Ours is hot nearly all the time, even in winter. We can get to the beach most times in the year. We never go short of sand, sea, sun . . . or fun! We do get rain sometimes, but when it comes . . . it never stays for long.

Now! We are bursting to show you our best

famous sights. We are most proud of them. It will be fun! Entao! (So!) Meet you at the aeroporto in um instante (one moment).

Ah, there you are! Have a good flight? Bom! (Good!) Now for your tour of our Cidade Maravilhosa. Please step in this luxury Mercedes kindly lent to us by Fernando Lisboa (our Dad).

First I would like to point you this lovely church on a perch. It is called Igreja da Penha.

"What an odd place for it!" you say. Well, here is why. One day a rich man and his family were having a piquenique (picnic) on top of that big rock. All of the sudden a big and perigoso (dangerous) snake came. It looked like they would be bited. The man fell on his knees and prayed to a saint to save them. Next moment a big lizard chased off the snake. They were saved! The man was well pleased. He said, "I will pay for a church to be built on this spot. To say 'Thank You!' to our saint." So that is why 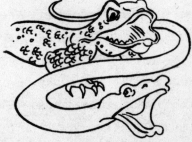 it is there. To see it close you must climb 365 steps – one for each day of the year.

Drive on Leo. Be careful! You know that Rio drivers are famous for craziness.

Now pen-friend. We bet you have seen a picture of this next very famous Rio sight before! It is the Pao de Acucar . . . the Sugar Loaf. But do not try to eat it. It is made of rock! It is named this because

of the clay pot that cane sugar juice is poured in to set hard to a "sugar loaf". When the tasty treat is taken out it is this shape. But the mountain is slightly bigger – 394 metres to the top (about as high as 1500 real sugar loaves on top of each other). Sometimes you see climbers clinging to its sides. Sim! They do this for fun! We won't go up this way. We will take the glass-walled cable-car to the top. It sways about but the view is fantastic.

Ah, at last we are at the top. Look – there is our Copacabana beach way down below us! And look over there. That is our other most famous sight.

The Corcovado (Hunchback) mountain with its gigantesco statue of Jesús Christ on the top. 30 metres tall! (25 times me!). At night he is lit by flood lights. It looks like he is floating in the sky. And he has got a great view of the football stadium too. There is green all

round Corcovado mountain. It's a jungle! That is where we are going next.

a good place to play hide and seek!

Ah, we are here! So what do you think? A tropical forest. Just minutes from the busy streets. We told you Rio was amazing! Our local jungle is called the Parque Nacional de Tijuca. It is not little.

It is big enough to be lost in. So always bring a map. It has got beautiful trees, rivers, waterfalls, mountains, all sorts of birds and animals. You will see swinging monkeys and lazy sloths all hanging out in here. But we can't hang about because it's the end of our tour. Just time to go to Copacabana beach for a refreshing sea dip . . . and maybe a game of futebol!

We hope that you enjoyed that bit of sightseeing. We must also tell you that there are some sad sights in Rio too. As well as all the rich people and medium people who live here there is also a very big lot of poor people. They live in houses made from old bits of metal and wood all put close together in little town places called favelas.

We are so lucky to live in our apartment.

Best wishes,

Maria and Leo

PS Have you got any places we would like?

34

12 Fevereiro (February)

Dear friend,

Hello there. How are you going? Anything big happening in your place? In Rio we are completely excited. We are nearly at our . . . CARNIVAL! The whole city is going happy crazy. It is also very hot. Today the big thermometer at the end of our street is saying 40°C. What's yours up to?

For us this time of year is more bigger and important than even Christmas! We started getting ready for it months ago. Now Carnival fever has grabbed us proper and good! At samba escola us dancers are practising till we drip. And our costume squad are sewing their dedos (fingers) off to make our outfits ready. We want our display to be the best! There'll be lots of other escolas in the big parade. The judges will be watching us like hawks when we put on our performance in the Sambadromo. That's the big stadium where we do our showing off. I hope we get first prize!

me
Daniela

Every year each dancing team has a different look for the show. This year ours is Rainforest. We will all be dressed as beautiful birds and animals and flowers. I will be a big Amazon water lily! This is our float.

Thousands of tourists come from all the world to join our fun.

Best wishes,
Maria

1 Marco (March)

Oi! Pen-fruit,

It's me, Leo! And me, Maria. How you going? Sorry we have been gone from you such a long time. We have been crazy busy with our Carnival things. But we hope you are feeling good. Leo's back is hurting. From carrying his big drum. And Maria has got blisters. From dancing all night long. Leo's hands are sore. From beating his big drum. And Maria's head fell off. No Leo, it didn't! My head-dress fell off. Oh yes! We had a great time. Now Carnival is done. For one more year. It was estupendo! But our escola did not win. And now we are flat. No! We are in our flat! Yes, that's it. Anyway, don't be sad that you missed it. Because we have drawn it for you. Hope you like it.

Best wishes,

Maria and Leo

My best bit. Dancing past the judges and TV cameras! I smiled to them so YOU could see ME!

Rubbish collecting men in bright orange uniforms danced and swept with their brushes.

Our mum, dancing and...

At the end. The men with big hosepipes. Blasting the dancers to cool them down.

... looking beautiful in her costume.

18 Março

Dear pen-pal,

It's me, Maria. Bom dia (good morning)! After
our Carnival excitements I wanted to write
from a place where things are peace and
quietful. But this is Rio! So that will not be
possible! Today for fun your letter is from my
diary! Hope you enjoy it!

10.30am – It is Saturday . . . BEACH DAY!
It is beautiful and sunny (as usual!). The surf
is sparkling. It seems like all of Rio is on the
sand. Thousands of people all over.
Every sort you can imagine. Large,
small, brown, black, white, poor and
rich. All together. Having a great
time! ← Oh no! Not Mr Anaconda too?! L.
OUR BIT OF BEACH – THE SCENE SO FAR.
I am writing. Mum is reading Jornal do Brasil
(her favourite newspaper). Dad is snoozing. He
went asleep as soon as he was in his
deckchair. He is snoring. Leo is hopping around
trying to keep his futebol in the air . . . and
squawking, like a parrot!

REST OF THE BEACH - THE SCENE SO FAR.
Doing, doing, doing! Too much to write. So I
will draw it too!

surfers
fresco ball
footvolei
Joggers
dancing to music
drinks
Tattooist
Food for sale

12.30pm – Lunchtime. We are at the beach
restaurant. We have just finished our feijoada
(we have it every Saturday!). It's Rio's
favourite dinner. And Leo's favourite! Made

from black beans and different
meats with slices of oranges on
top. Sometimes with pigs' ears
and tails and noses. But I
prefer it without.

And I prefer it with. Snort snort grunt! L.

3pm – Back on the beach. Dad and Leo are
playing volleyball with some neighbours. Dad's
showing off his "skills". Lots of leaping and
diving. Opa! He has fallen on his face. A bit
embarrassing for him.

But funny for everyone else! L.

3.30pm – Leo is
begging me to jog
with him. Oh well, I
suppose I'll keep
him company. It's
fun to splash in the

surf. I can check out the library when we
stop for a rest (yes, we've even got those on
our beach!).

4pm – I'm back from the jog. Leo was playing
football with two boys he met when I was
looking at books.

6pm – The beach is emptying fast. We're all
heading for our apartment. Why? Because
everyone wants to be back for the
supernovela! I think you call it soap? People
in Brazil are mad on them. Our most favourite
is "Sempre Tem Jeito" ("There's Always A
Way"). It would be. It's the one Mum's TV
company makes! After, I must practise my
dancing. We have got
200 different radio
stations in Rio. I
always have plenty of
music to choose
from. I must be
careful to save some energy for our bike ride
in Tijuca Forest tomorrow.

Bye for now, and great big waves,

Maria

2 Abril (April)

Oi!

It's me Leo – your pal from Rio! Are you getting up to loads of action stuff? I'm not! I have been hit by a mischief! I fell off my bicicleta

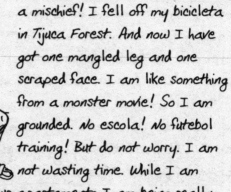

in Tijuca Forest. And now I have got one mangled leg and one scraped face. I am like something from a monster movie! So I am grounded. No escola! No futebol training! But do not worry. I am not wasting time. While I am stitched up in our apartamento I am being really useful to you. Just for you I have been finding out...

HOW THE AMAZON RIVER GOT ITS NAME

One day some Portuguese explorers were going up this huge river (which they didn't know what to call). They met some really fierce warriors and had a battle with them. Then they went back and told their friends about them. This is how it happened:

44

Some people think that the fierce warriors weren't women but just looked like them because of how they were dressed. Maybe the Portuguese weren't wearing their spectacles?

Hey, I'm learning stuff with my brilhante letters to you! When I go back to school Mr Anaconda will be stunned! Maybe I will be put on top of the classroom?

More amazing writes coming soon.

Best regards from your pain-friend,

Leo

PS Maria says I had my crash because I was showing off my famous cycling-with-hands-on-head trick. Not true! I was scared from my wits by a thing which came out from behind a bush! I think it was maybe a . . . a . . . gousti!

12 Abril

Hi there dear pen-friend,

It's Maria. How are you? Perhaps you are still wondering what is this misterioso (mysterious) "gousti" thing that scared the life from my poor brother? A horrible Brazilian spook? A terrible forest monster? No! It was a furry little creature - called an agouti! Yes! He got his spelling wrong. Sorry for his mistake.

I think that when we go on our jungle holiday we will see lots more agoutis. And many other creatures even more surprising than them! Just with frogs alone the rainforest has  got more than 300 sorts! With some that whistle. And some that bark. And some that go moo! Also there are 250 different sorts of mammals. And 3,000 kinds of fish! As part of my getting ready I have found out about these different creatures. And I am totalmente carried along by this great topico.

Here is just one page of my work book with some amazing animals for your interest. . .

A Page From My Rainforest Nature Book -
Drawn and Written By M. Lisboa

First, my brother's furry friend. . .

The Agouti — They are partly like a guinea pig and partly like a rat. With long legs and a tiny tail. Also as big as a little dog - about 50 centimetres long.

Yes . . . it was one of these that jumped out at me. L.

The Glass Frog — This is not made from glass but you can see right through its skin! You can watch all its inside bits working . . . its heart beating, all the stomach bits and pieces doing their stuff, and its green bones joined up for its skeleton!

The Horned Toad – It is like a creature from a monster movie! It is very big with horns and a big mouth. It is quite fierce and eats other frogs and small mammals.

croak croak!

The Vampire Bat – This is a creature from a monster movie! It runs along the ground to a sleeping mammal – maybe a pig or a cow – then sinks its teeth in. But only very gently, so it doesn't wake them up. Then it drinks the trickling blood! Uncle Jesus says to take no notice of the Dracula stories. Vampire bats don't often bother humans much.

The Giant Armadillo – This looks like a reptile but it is a mammal. They are 1.5 metres long. That's as big as Leo! They go into a ball to protect themselves from their enemies. Forest Indians like to eat them. There used to be an even bigger one. Its shell was 3 metres long and the Indians used them for roofs on their houses! But we don't have these any more.

Maybe they all got turned into house roofs? L.

<u>The Aruana Fish</u> — When this fish sees a spider or an insect sitting on a tree branch above the water it doesn't think, "Oh what a pity. I would like to eat that tasty thing but I cannot reach it!" Instead, it leaps right out of the water, grabs the creature from the tree . . . and gobbles it up!

<u>The Jaguar</u> — Mostly these are golden brown with black spots but sometimes they are black all over. They are very shy and only attack humans every now and again.

They are "endangered" (there aren't many left) because people kill them for their lovely skins. Uncle is really angry about this.

<u>The Electric Eel</u> – This kills other creatures with a big electricity shock. Then it eats them! Some people think it uses its electricity to shake fruit from trees as well.

These are only just a few of the creatures that are in the rainforest. I don't suppose we are going to see them all. Uncle says that even though there are many animals people are sometimes disappointed because they hardly see them at all in the forest! This is because many creatures are very shy and spend their time hiding or have got good camouflage. He says that he will try and make sure we see plenty!

Best wishes,

Maria

15 maio (May)

Oi! Penalty-friend!

How you dribbling? I am very, very happy today. For two things!

First one — I am better from my acidente (accident). Yesss! My leg is completely mended. Second one — Tonight we are all going to the "Fla-Flu"! It will be brilhante! It is a VERY importante futebol match for all of us in Rio. Our top two futebol teams, Flamengo and Fluminese, are going to have their battle in front of all the home fans at Maracana Stadium. Everyone will go. The crowds will be massive and squashing. Lucky for us Maracana is massive too. But not squashing! There is room for nearly 200,000 people! I just cannot wait to get there to support my top team . . .
FLAMENGO! FLAMENGO! FLAMENGO! FLAMENGO! FLAMENGO!

Who is your favourite? Or maybe you aren't futebol crazy, like me? Perhaps you are just an "off it, on it" fan, like my twin sister? Or maybe you even think it is boring? If you do I think that you are mad! Sorry, not really. Listen! If you come to a soccer game in Brazil you will never be bored! Even if you don't like futebol not at all. Because our matches are all . . . ESTUPENDO! Right! Now I will go and put on my Flamengo kitten.

Your top striker,

Leo .. GOOOOOOLEO! GOOOOOOLEO!
FLAMENGO! GO! GO! GO! GO! LEO!

PS Please do not worry. Leo is wearing Flamengo futebol kit - not a kitten! M.

53

16 Maio

Dear pen-pal,

Bom dia! How are you? The futebol match was fantastico! (fantastic!) And - even with 150,000 crazy Cariocas going wild around me! - I managed to write you my action report. So here it is, with some handy tips (like this: <u>HT</u>).

Fantastico Futebol From Brazil
Live And Kicking - by Maria Lisboa

7.15pm - The crowd is going wild. Cheering, chanting, singing, waving giant, coloured banners, sending up fire balloons, letting off fireworks . . . the lot! My brother is shouting and dancing.

And now the teams are coming out! Oh, sorry! Did I tell you the game hasn't started yet? Yes, it's always the same. More like a football party than a football match!

<u>HT</u> If you can't be bothered with the football, just watch the crowd. There's always lots of action!

7.45pm – The game is on! I can hardly think because of the shouting and singing. On top of that thousands of fans are beating giant samba drums non-stop!

Now someone has thrown a smoke bomb (with smoke in Flamengo colours of course!).

<u>HT</u> Take your earplugs to the game if you cannot stand big noise.

8.00pm – It is already two goals each. The action is really hotting up. And the fans are

getting very, very happy.
They are throwing
things . . . toilet rolls,
party streamers, even
dead chickens! Yes,
people are throwing
them on to the pitch.

Eeeeek!

HT Take care where
you sit at our football matches.

8.50pm — It is still 2-2. Leo and Mum and
Dad are all shouting themselves hoarsey. A
Flamengo player does a brilhante dribble. The
drums are beating faster. He has got past
four opponents! My parents and my brother
(plus 80,000 other Flamengo fans) all jump
from their seats and yell "OLÉ! OLÉ! OLÉ!
OLÉ!". The Flamengo man passes to his striker.
The striker scores!

Leo leaps again - at least three metres into the air this time! He yells:

GOOOOOOOOOL!

I am timing his shout. Eight seconds (not bad - his record is 11). He falls. On top of me!
10.20pm - We are driving home. After much jumping about, yelling, finger-nail biting, groaning and gasping from the fans the game has ended 4-2 for Flamengo. My family are trying to sing their supporters' song - but just croaks are coming out.
HT Remember to take some throat sweets.

I hope you enjoyed that match. It will probably be our last big one to see before we go to the Amazon. I am glad it was a scorcher!

Best wishes,

Maria

16 Junho (June)

Oi . . . pen-top!

It's me, Leo, the Copacabanana Kid! How you jumping in? We are fine but at escola this week we have been working our necks off! The other day we told Mr Anaconda a bit more about our big trip. Since then it feels like he has gone Amazon crazy. He is exploding with it! Between you and we - we guess he is a bit jealous of us. M. But we don't mind! It's fun! Today river facts were pouring out from him like he had bursted his brain banks. Dive into this and you'll see what I mean!

THE AMAZING AMAZON BY LEO LISBOA (WHO IS ALSO QUITE AMAZING)

* The Amazon is 6,280 kilometres long. It is the second longest river in the world (so we won't have time to go right along it). Do you know the longest?

* Every one second 10,000,000,000 (ten billion) litres of water pour from the Amazon into the Atlantic Ocean!

* This fresh water and a load of mud and stuff called sediment blasts into the ocean. It goes in with such big power that there is still a massive muddy brown patch of it 100 miles from the coast.

* When the Italian explorer, Amerigo Vespucci was sailing in the Atlantic 500 years ago he spotted the muddy brown waves.

And that's how he found the Amazon . . . and Brazil!

* In many places the Amazon is between 6 and 10 kilometres from one side to the other. When you are on it you often cannot see the banks. It goes even wider when it is flooded.

* It begins as a little dribble in the Andes mountains. But where it meets the sea its mouth is wider than all the way from Paris in France to London in Britain! There is an island in this bit that is as big as all of Switzerland.

* After the big rains from Janeiro to Maio (our words for January and May) the flood waters rush down to the ocean. But, the ocean waves are on their way up to meet the river! So they have a heads on crash . . .
KERPOWSPLOOSHSPLOSH! There is roaring like thunder and great churning and wild fighting between the waters. It is amazing to see. The ocean wins the battle. So then the flood waters race back up the river in a big wave which goes at 25 kilometres per hour. This is called the Pororoca.
* There are more than one thousand other rivers joining on to the Amazon. They are called its tributaries. Some are more than 1,600 kilometres long. That is four times longer than the River Thames in the UK! (That is just a trickle!)

The Mighty Amazon

Now you have read this you might know more about this great river than your own teacher does. Give them a quiz! You will leave them bottom of the class . . . and Amazon!

All of this I have remembered from Mr Anaconda's talk. Do you think I am turning into a brainbox? Maybe I could be a top teacher? And a great footballer! And a musica star!

Best wishes from your totalmente brilhante buddy,

Professor Leo Lisboa

25 Junho

Dear good friend,

Bom dia. How are you? This time in two weeks
we will be in the Amazon rainforest. Yesterday
Uncle came to chat about our trip. It was
fun. We felt like old-days explorers getting
ready to visit a strange new world!

He gave us his special tips about jungle living
so we will be sound and safe. It is very
different to apartment living! After that he told
us how we will fly from Rio then travel in lots
of different sorts of boats. We have made you
a map of our route so you can track us.
Here it is!

OUR STOPPING AND STARTING PLACES

A - RIO

B - MANAUS

C - A SECRET! (only Uncle Jesus knows what it will be!)

D - A CAMPING SPOT IN THE JUNGLE

OUR TRANSPORTINGS

① A big jet plane - fast!

② A big river boat - medium-slow.

③ A small canoe - very slow.

* People from other countries call this river the Amazon too, but Brazil people call it Rio Solimoes.

The other thing we talked about was things to take. I think Uncle has got most of the stuff already but we made a list anyway. I was in charge of writing it. Here are some of the things I put down:

Amazon Rainforest trip. Do not forget. . .

Ponchos – do you have these? We are taking water-proof ones – it can get very rainy in the jungle.
It's a rainforest! L.

Hammocks (redes) – for sleeping in. They keep you off the floor away from creepy crawlies and damp. The Indians invented these and lots of other people in the world have borrowed this intelligent idea. Have you ever been in one?

Fishing tackle — net, line, hooks - for catching fish for us to eat.

Mosquito net — not for catching mosquitoes to eat! To go over our hammocks . . . so the mosquitoes don't eat us!

Can't bite me now Mr Mossie!

Malaria tablets — to stop us getting the horrible malaria disease from mosquito bites.

Cotton shirts — long sleeves, to protect our arm skin from sun and insects.

Trousers — with tying strings on the ankles to stop the bugs climbing up our legs and biting us in personal places!

Cream for insects — to keep them off us. We rub it over us - not them!

BUZZ OFF

Flashlights and headlamps — for going on walks in the jungle at night.

Some rope and a padlock — for fastening the boat up to a tree at night. So no one steals it.

Some more rope — for hanging up our hammocks.

Woollen blankets — yes! Uncle says it can get chilly at night!

Straps and strings — to hang up our bags so the animals don't get in them.

<u>Backpack</u> – for carrying
stuff – must be
waterproof of course.
<u>Life jackets</u> – in case
boat tips over.
<u>Compass</u> – so we don't get lost.
<u>Other stuff</u> – maps; tent; torch; pocket
knife; candles; camera; insect repeller; water
carrier; binoculars (to look at wildlife); pouch
belt – to keep money in.

It's a lot, isn't it? Uncle says we will be
staying in all sorts of places. Some top class
luxury five-star, and some real tough, no stars.
And no electricity or toilet!

↑
Just the ones
in the sky! L.

All the best,

Maria

PS While we were making the list Leo asked
Uncle if he should bring along his soccer
boots!! Sometimes my brother leaves my mouth
empty for words! *You never know – I might meet some
Indians who want me to teach them my fine skills? L.*

2 Julho (July)

Oi! It's Leo,

How you doing? I am fine! Today at escola I have done all my class a big favour. This morning Mr Anaconda planned a big maths test. But no one had done the work! As soon as Mr Anaconda had finished register I said, "Senhor Silva. I am expecting to bump into some Indians in the rainforest. Could you tell us about them, por favor (please)?" He went into action imediatemente (immediately). Like a top goalkeeper. I shot questions. He dived for them!

Senhor Silva - top goalkeeper!

What a save!

He told us loads. All really interesting! By the time he was finished it was too late to do our sums. Yesss! The whole class was smiling at me. Right from its one ear to the other! I am so pleased with me I have put some Mr Anaconda facts here for you. . .

The Indians Who Live In The Rainforest

Questions by me, answers by Mr Anaconda

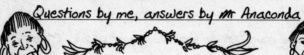

me – Where did the Indians first come from Mr Ana . . . err, Mr Silva!

Mr A. – They came from Siberia and crossed to Alaska when those two countries were joined together. This was probably about 60,000 years ago but no one is exactly sure.

SIBERIA
(route taken by the Siberians)

Two continents were joined here

North America

South America

me – But how did they get all the way to South America?

Mr A. – They walked! But very slowly – only about 16 kilometres a year! All the time some of them were stopping and settling and becoming different sorts of Indian tribes in North America. But others were carrying on south. Eventually some of these got to the rainforest about 15,000 years ago. They began living from it by hunting and collecting fruit and growing stuff. They are still there now and are still doing many of the things they were doing all that time ago.

me – What sort of things?

mr A. – They put poison from vines or crushed herbs in the river to catch fish. This stops the fish from swimming or knocks them out. After this they trap them in nets made from reeds. Sometimes they just get the fish by shooting arrows into them.

me – So, are they dangerous?

mr A. – They have attacked people but it is usually to defend their forest from land stealers who want to cut it down and burn it. Long ago when the Portuguese were first coming here one tribe caught a bishop and ate him. This got all the other Indians a bad name.

me – Uncle Jesus says he thinks they should be left in peace to live their forest life.

Mr A. – Yes. Me too! A lot of people think that the way of life they are living is good. It doesn't do harm to the environment.

Me – Are there many left?

Mr A. – No one knows how many Indians there are in the rain forest because there are parts of it that still haven't been explored. Some people think there might be about 50 tribes who have still *never met* people from the modern world.

Me – Oba! (Wow!) Maybe we will bump into them?

All of Class – Ha ha ha ha ha!

Ha   Ha   He He
Oba!   Ha Ha   My brother, he's CRAZY!
Ha   Ha   Ho Ho
Ha Ha

Best of all wishes,

Leo

PS I've just remembered something else! Mr Anaconda says that some of the Indians are futebol crazy. They will play even if they haven't got a ball. They use a coconut. A bit tough for headers I think!

4 Julho

Dear pen pal,

How are you? It's us - Maria and Leo from Rio! Bet
you wish you were us. Only four days to go. We are
buzzy as bees. No time even for futebol for Leo. We
mustn't forget one thing. Because we cannot buy it
in the jungle. There are no shops. Uncle says "No
good being up the river without your piddle." Oops,
I think that should be paddle. He also says we must
think about being safe and keeping good health.
The jungle can be very bad to you. Mum is glad we
are going with him. She knows he will take good
care of us. She says, "My clever brother Jesus is
the expert on everything." She is nearly right – he
knows hardly one thing about futebol and nothing
about samba.

As well as malaria tablets we have got lots of
other first aid medicines. There are many bad
jungle things you can get wrong with you. We must
be careful. There are insectos all over the place.
They like to jab you with their stingers and give
you diseases. But we have beat them to
it. Our doctor has jabbed us with his
needle first! For protection. Owch!

Leo is scared to meet snakes. But I don't think they will be too pleased about bumping into him! But Uncle says don't worry. Just be sensible and careful. Here are his snake tips and informations for you.

Maybe they will come in useful for your snakes where you live. Or for your Amazon adventure when you come?

1) They are scared of us. They only attack you if you tread on them or upset them. So Leo must not call them bad names!

2) A lot of poisonous ones are tiny tiny. As small as a little shoe lace! They can get in your shoe or your back-pack or your hammock. So before you use it make sure you

give all your stuff a really, really good shake. And keep it fastened all the time.

3) After it has rained be extra careful. A very deadly snake or scorpion or spider might have nipped into your hut or your shoe to take shelter. So check it out!

4) If you get a bite:

*Do not suck it like they do in the movies. The poison will go back in your blood.

*Try to see what sort of snake has got you. Grown-ups sometimes catch them after a biting. Not a good idea for children! This is so the doctor will know what sort of snake-bite medicine to give you.

Last tips. Uncle says we must not touch any creep crawlies at all. The Amazon has even got caterpillars that bite you. And you can get fever from some bees. There are dangerous ants and things all over the forest floor. So we must also never go about with bare feet. You can Leo. Your foot smell will knock them all out! I think the jungle is a tricky place!

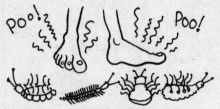

The Indians managed to stay living there for 15,000 years with no tablets or jabs because they use the forest plants for medicine.

OK! We are going to inspect our socks. We hope you are in good health.

Take care,

Maria and Leo (The twins from Brazil.)

PS Our next letter to you will be from THE AMAZON!

5 Julho

Dear friend of the twins,

Hi to you. I hope that the birds are singing where you are and that you are feeling real good! I am Maria and Leo's Uncle Jesus (you say "Shaysoos"). Maria said I should tell you a bit about myself. I hope you don't mind!

One of the things that I am is an entomologist - this means I study insects. Brazil is a great place to do this. We have got thousands and thousands of them here, especially in the rainforest.

Probably about 150,000 different sorts altogether! Or maybe even as many as 60,000,000 (60 million)! No one knows for sure. Most of them have not got names yet. I have discovered and named quite a few but I will never finish this huge job in my life!

Maybe Maria will take over from me. I am also a wildlife artist. I like to make pictures of all kinds of creatures - big ones as well as little ones. On my next page is a picture for you:

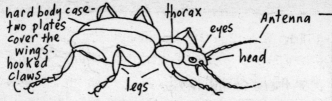

hard body case—
two plates
cover the
wings.
hooked
claws
legs
thorax
eyes
Antenna
head

I am an environmentalist too. This means I try to help save the rainforest and its animals and people from some of the bad things that are happening to them. Maybe you know about the problems from your TV and school? Sadly the forest is being destroyed by thoughtless people because they want its space for their crops and mines and cows.

burning the forest for farm land

logging

They don't care how they get rid of the jungle! They spray deadly poison over it from aeroplanes! Cut down the trees! Burn it! Drive giant tractors through it! All kinds! It doesn't matter what, as long as it is quickest and cheapest for them! And it is all to make things that we all want to buy.

DON'T WE REALIZE THAT THE FOREST IS OUR BIG AND IMPORTANT TREASURE-HOUSE OF NATURE? IT HAS GOT MORE DIFFERENT SORTS OF LIVING THINGS THAN ANYWHERE ELSE ON OUR PLANET! ONCE THE FORESTS ARE GONE WE CAN NEVER HAVE THEM BACK! WE ARE ALL BIG ESTUPIDOS!

I'm sorry. It makes me get very angry. You see, ever since I was born 35 years ago, this destruction was happening. I also know that it is still not too late to save the forest. That is why I organize protests and sometimes am on the TV to let people know what is going on.

Best wishes,

Uncle Jesus

PS Please forgive me for shouting at you!

8 Julho

Dear pal,

A quick note. Yes! We are here. At last! Really at the Amazon rainforest. Not right in the jungle yet but in a big hotel in the main city, Manaus. It is very noisy. I don't think that will stop me sleeping.

Our flight from Rio to here took many hours. Brazil is gigantesco! Maria and Uncle are asleep already. Only my excitement is keeping me awake.

For now please enjoy the scene on my "cartao postal" (post card):

This is where the Rio Solimoes joins the Rio Negro. It flows like this for quite some way. One side of it is black coffee with no milk, the other one coffee with cream! After a while they get all mixed up. Just like my brain is now! Sleep tights! Leo

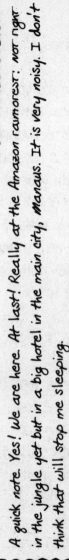

BRAZIL POST 50

79

9 Julho

Dear pen-friend of the twins,

Hello! It's me, Jesus. How are you? I'm feeling
fine. I've had my sleep now but Leo and Maria are
still in bed. While they are recovering I will tell you
a story. But first, here is a question. When you
are drawing or writing with your pencil and make a
mistake do you use a rubber to make it disappear?
I think so. Or do you never make mistakes? Once
upon a time many people here in Manaus became
very, very rich, all because of the stuff that your
rubber is made from! Here is how:

THE STORY OF THE TREE THAT CRIES

In the rainforest there is a tree the
Indians call a seringa - "the tree
that cries" - because sticky sap
stuff dribbles from it when you cut
it. The Indians make a slit in the
tree and put a bowl beneath it to
catch the liquid like this...
   They have used the sap to make
bouncy balls and water holders for as long as

they can remember. Yes! It is what we call rubber!

About a hundred years ago factories in the USA and Europe began making things 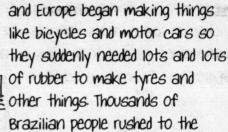 like bicycles and motor cars so they suddenly needed lots and lots of rubber to make tyres and other things. Thousands of Brazilian people rushed to the jungle to get the rubber so they could sell it and get lots of money. Sadly, it wasn't them that got all the money for the rubber. It was the people who owned the land. They got richer and richer and richer by using the other people and the Indians as slaves to get it for them. They got so rich that they could afford to light their cigars with $100 notes!

Then one day it all finished! Because of a crafty Englishman called Henry Wickham. Henry went into the forest with some Indians and picked up 70,000 seeds. Henry hid them between banana leaves and took them on a boat to England as fast as he could.

Then he took them to a country called Malaysia on the other side of the world. The trees grew much better there and it was easier for ships to get near the plantations. So the factories began

buying rubber from Malaysia instead. And that was the end of the big money for the Brazil rubber bosses!

Tomorrow I will take the twins to see the beautiful Opera House that the rich guys had built here. They even had rubber put in the road in front of it so that the audience would not hear the noise of the horses and carriages outside.

We will go by boat to our next place. That is a secret surprise for the twins. I think they will be very happy when they get there!

Uncle Jesus

10 Julho

Dear pen-friend,

Good morning. It's me, Maria. How's things?
Are you enjoying some quiet and peace? I
wish I was! We are at Porto do Manaus (the
port of Manaus) on the bank of the River
Negro. It is crazy! Copacabana is a sleepy
village next to here! And I am sitting on a box
in the middle of a mad bustle and hustle trying
my best to put it in words and pictures for
you.

We are waiting for our boat to be mended. We've been on it once. But now we're off it again! It went a short way from the port but then there was big smoke from the engine and KERBOOM! After that there was wild shouting and running about by the boatmen. We had to turn around and come back. Uncle said it could take quite a few hours to put right, so he is reading his insect book to pass the time. A boy is trying to sell him a chicken. I don't think he wants it. It's still alive! Leo is watching a stall woman barbecuing some fish. He looks as hungry as I feel.

Senhor, you want a nice chicken?

The noise here is deafening. People are yelling at each other. The boat captains are honking their fog horns like crazy. (Don't ask me why – there's no fog!) All the boat engines are clattering and roaring (apart from ours!). The

Honk honk!

air is filled with smoke. There are grunting

grunt grunt!

hens and clucking pigs all over the place. (They like their food fresh here.) Men are throwing bananas at each other and shouting angrily. I just hope they don't start

cluck!

cluck!

fighting! Hundreds of people are pushing and shoving to get on and off the boats all at the same time. It is like the whole place has gone . . . bananas? And it is also very stinky!

Look out! Flying bananas!

Uncle won't even tell us where we're going next! He also says we must wear our life-jackets when we are on the boat. Sometimes they flip right over!

I hope this will not be my last ever letter to you!

Best wishes,

Maria

PS Slightly better news. Here come Uncle and Leo with some grilled chicken. (So, did he buy that bird after all?)

PPS I've just understood something – the men are unloading the bananas. Not trying to kill each other with them!

12 Julho

Oi – Pen nib!

How you dripping? Sim! It's me . . . Leo on the Rio!
We are now back on our big boat. Chug chug-a-
lugging up the Rio Negro. But Uncle still won't tell us
where to! Perhaps he doesn't know! Hope he does!
   There are hundreds of boats going up and down
this gigantesco water road – all kinds of traffic.
Look what I've seen already. . .

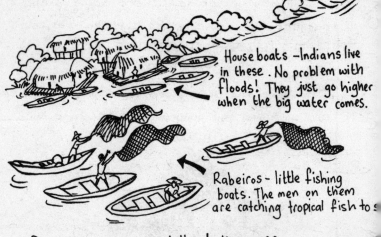

House boats – Indians live
in these. No problem with
floods! They just go higher
when the big water comes.

Rabeiros – little fishing
boats. The men on them
are catching tropical fish to s

Dug out canoes – what the Indians use
Just a tree trunk hollowed out by
chipping with an axe. They are
the first boats ever used on
the   Amazon.

Barqueiros - boatmen, everywhere.

Caboclos - people who live in the villages on the river banks.

Flat bottom boats - if they get stuck on the sand banks they are easy to push off. But also easy to tip over!

Army boat full of soldiers going to a jungle station in the middle of nowhere.

Little tourist boats - wooden with a roof made of palm leaves - nice and shady.

Now! One great thing about our boat. It has got satellite TV! There is a futebol match just starting on it right now! I'm . . . GONE!

Leo

15 Julho

Dear friend,

Bom dia from Maria! How are you? I am feeling a little bit happier than when I last spoke to you. We are right up the river now! Just about here!

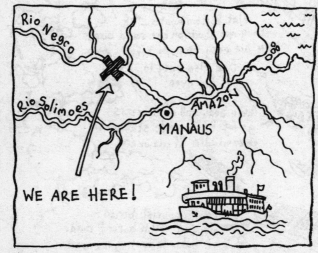

And we haven't sunk once! This boat trip is better than I thought it was going to be. And very interesting!

Listen to this! After we left the port again there was another big fuss! This time a thief was trying to steal someone's wallet. He got sorted out real quick. I don't think he wanted

to go swimming. But he had no choice! The wallet man and some other passengers threw him straight in the river! Leo said, "Serves him right!" I felt sorry for him. The last thing we saw was him swimming to the bank as fast as he could. I didn't see any alligators. But you never know!

This boat is not comfortable like our top five-star luxury hotel in Manaus was. So I think I will give it minus half a star! Everyone sleeps in their hammocks which are strung up on the decks. At night there are sleeping people hanging everywhere. It feels like we are part of a big family of human bats. It is quite good fun really. But I don't think I would like to do it for ever!

It is a bit difficult for us to sleep because the man in the next hammock has got his goat  with him. They are both very noisy and very smelly. We can't decide who stinks worse, the man, or his goat! (Oops! I hope he can't see what I'm writing!) At least Uncle knew to hang our hammocks near the front of the boat. Away from the toilets. Their smell was even more bad!

Until yesterday the most wildlife we had seen were the fleas on our neighbour's goat. Then we saw the botos (river dolphins). They are brilhante! Just like the fleas, they are great jumpers. They leap from the river with big snorts.

They are also supposed to be very brainy. Uncle says that the people who live round here believe they have magic powers. They say that sometimes the botos leave the river and turn themselves into smart men in white suits who charm away the local girls.

I am beginning to enjoy my holiday a bit now. And I don't mind the uncomforts too much.

Yours from a long way up the Amazon,

Maria

PS We saw a man in a white suit on the river bank this afternoon! He waved to us as we went past! He was a dolphin looking for a sweetheart. No doubt at all.

17 Julho

Dear pen-pally!

Oi! Greetings from . . . *AMAZON TOWERS!* Yes. This
is where we are. A hotel stuck up poles. It's *otimo*
(great)! This was Uncle's big secret for us. *Oba*
(Wow)! It feels like we have turned to parrots.
Living up a tree. No joke. Right on top of the forest!
And in the best room. It is called *Tarzan House*.
(Do you know his films?)

When we got here our eyes went . . . POP! We
throwed our stuff in our rooms and rushed to explore.
All really easy. There are staircases and bridges
between the towers and the trees. Even if the forest
is flooded you can enjoy the sights. We checked out
the wildlife. There is loads! A woolley monkey
jumped off a branch on to my shoulder and put its

tail around my neck. "It thinks
you're its long lost cousin from
Rio!" said Uncle. Lucky it was
friendly. Sometimes they won't

I think she likes me!

let go. And bite your head! Just afterwards a

coatimundi tried to steal Uncle's
binoculars. Now we laughed. (A
coatimundi is like a racoon.)

Last night we had our dinner in the
treetop restaurant. It has a screen to stop monkeys
jumping in and pinching food! All they could do was
sit sad in the trees and watch us eat. Just like at
the zoo. But with us in the cage and them the
visitors!

As well as all the treetop stuff the hotel has got a
swimming pool and a heli-pad! I will beg on my knees
to Uncle Jesus to take us for a helicopter spin. I will
have to work fast. We are only here for four days.

Speak to you soon!

Tarzan Lisboa

18 Julho

Dear pen-friend down on the ground,

I have spent my morning on our hotel balcony doing you this drawing of the rainforest.

Black Spider monkeys.

The floor at the bottom...

Armadillos and tapirs and giant toads and things live here. There are masses of ants and termites roaming around.

Yellow headed Vultures and Cocoa thrushes flying over the top.

This is the main top part (I can touch it from my balcony!).
It is called the 'canopy'. It gets all the sunshine and rain. Most of the animals and birds live here.

A strange half boy, half monkey creature.
(I think she means me! L.)

The middle is called the 'understorey'. It is gloomy and dark. Young plants that don't need much light grow here. There are also lianas which grow up the tree trunks and branches, like living ropes.

These trees are called 'emergent' trees. Their roots spread really wide and help keep all the soil in one place.

At the bottom the leaves and branches rot down to soil very quickly because of the heat and damp and the insects munching them non-stop. This makes the soil full of food for the trees. They suck it up with their roots so that they can grow really big. Then drop their leaves and branches to the floor again. So that they can rot again. And be munched again!

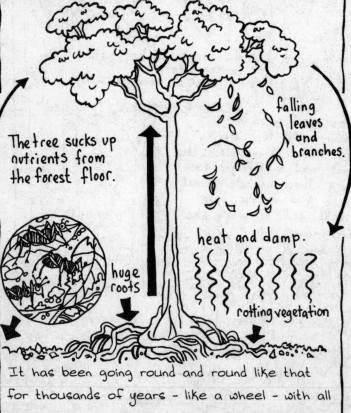

The tree sucks up nutrients from the forest floor.

falling leaves and branches.

heat and damp.

huge roots

rotting vegetation

It has been going round and round like that for thousands of years - like a wheel - with all the animals and plants doing their bit. They all need each other. Each one gives something to the others. Uncle says that this is called an ecosystem. Leo has just said that it makes him think of a football team (what doesn't!). *All the members need each other. Take one away and the rest are in trouble. L.*

Uncle says we should make the most of our time here. After this things might be a bit tougher! We are going up a small side-river in a canoe to do a few days' camping in the wild.

We'll write to you – if we are still one piece!

Best wishes,

Maria

PS This is a giant toad. Have you ever seen one? They can be 38 centimetres from their nose to their bottom. We saw one from the walkways today. It was as big as my CD player! MASSIVE! Uncle says they make a rumbling like thunder in their throat. He has seen them going to houses and stealing the dog and cat food straight from their plates!

20 Julho

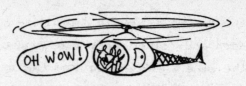

Dear pal,

GOOOLAAA! My wish came true! We went up in the helicopter. It wasn't for too long. But . . . it was estupendo!

We had a bird's-beak view of the whole rainforest. Well, I thought it was the whole rainforest. But Uncle has told us that we were looking at only a tiny bit. Even though it was stretching as far as our eyes could see.

Trees as far as the eye can see!

He says that our Brazil part of the rainforest is enormous. It covers half of our whole country and

100

spreads over 3,000,000 (three million) square
kilometres. That is so massively big that you could fit
the whole country of Germany into it nearly eight
times! Lots of it has never ever been explored. It is
called the mata fechada (closed forest). It is a very
tough place to go. Some people call it "Green Hell".
I could see why. Everywhere I looked was green
green green in every direction, with just the rivers
running through it, twisting and turning like massive
brown snakes! Now I can see why the Indians say
that the Amazon River is just a very big anaconda!

Best wishes,

Leo

PS I think I have just
upset my Uncle. A big
feroz (ferocious) insect
came in our room. So I
drummed it with my shoe.
BLATT! KERCHOW! BLATT! until it was dead. When
Uncle saw it he was really zangado (angry). He said it
was a very special beetle sort that he has not seen
ever before. Now he cannot take it back because I
have made it entirely flat.

22 Julho

Dear pen-pal,

Are you safe and smug in your house with your door tight shut and your TV on? Wish I was! Tonight is our very first night outside in the jungle. I am terrified! It feels like we are a billion miles from modern things. Maybe even on another planet! No telephones, no hotels, no roads, no nothing! Just us and a massive lot of wild NATURE!

I am so glad that Uncle Jesus is here! He has made a little fire to cook our food and make us cheerful. He says it will keep big wild animals like the jaguars away if they are getting too interested! I am using its flame light to write you this letter.

There are hundreds of jungle night-noises around us. Uncle knows them all!

First, clicks, rattles and whistles. "That's tree frogs," he says.

Then loud "thrut thrut thrut".

"Crickets!" says Uncle.

And then "ping ping ping!" (quite soft).

"That's the bats," Uncle has told us.

"They are echolocating. They send their ping sound out. It bounces back to them from things and they know where they are!" And at the back of all this, thousands of other insects, all going, "chk clik chk chk chu clk".

"The whole lot together sounds like a big

samba bateria to me!" said Leo. "With a thousand little drummers playing on a thousand little drums!"

"You're right!" said Uncle. "I prefer it to noisy cities and car horns, any time!"

"Maybe you do." I said, "But you are used to it!"

Leo was tapping a samba rhythm on his tea mug and Uncle was joining him with his spoon on his bowl when suddenly we heard:

It was right behind me! I nearly shot past my skin.

"What's that!?" I cried.

"Only a rat," said Uncle.

"A rat that barks?" said Leo.

"Yes," said Uncle. "It is called the cora rat. It's nothing to worry about!"

And then, about half an hour ago we heard a very odd noise. "Woosh woosh wooooooo

wooooooo woooooosh wooooersh woooo
wooooooh," like that.

"So, what's that one?" said Leo.

"I don't know that one," said Uncle. "Maybe it
is Curupira come to see us."

"Who's he?" laughed Leo. "A friend of yours?"

"No!" said Uncle. "He is the Bogey Man of
the jungle!"

The hair prickled on my neck and Leo's
eyes went very big in the firelight. Like he was
going to cry! "You are joking . . . aren't you?"
he said.

"I think I am." said Uncle with a smile.
"When the Indians hear a noise that they

don't know, they say it is
Curupira. He is one of
their ghosts! They say
that Curupira is a short
and hairy ghost and he
has got feet that point
backwards. He calls
children by whistling to
them or making the winds
blow. When they hear his noise they cannot
stop themselves going to him. Then he takes
them into the deepest part of the forest and

they are never ever seen again!"

After Uncle said this Leo went very quiet and thoughtful. And later on when the whooshing noise came back a bit I saw him putting his fingers in his ears!

I hope Curupira is just a story. We are going to our hammocks soon but I am not too easy. I have got an all over creepy feeling that we are being watched. Uh oh! I hope I can sleep.

Signing off. Hoping for a safe night.

Your best pal in a hammock,

Maria

PS Wish you were here. (But do you?)

PPS A new noise has just come! Like this . . . "hisss hissss hissss hisssss!"

"Is that snakes?!" Leo said.

"No, it's the giant cockroaches!" Uncle told him. "They are hissing ones."

27 Julho

Oi pen!

How you going? For us it is day number five in the jungle. Our holiday is whizzing past! But we are really used to wild living now. No things bother us! Not even the gang of howler monkeys who scream above us some nights! When we first heard them I was so frightened. I fell right out of my hammock! Now we just pretend they are the teenagers who shout about near our street in Rio. They are showing off to other howler gangs. Maybe just like teenagers?

This morning we saw a big flash of red and yellow in the trees. It was a toucan.

"How does it fly with that big beak stuck to its face?" I said.

"The beak is *not* heavy at all," said Uncle. "If toucans could *not* get about it would be bad for the rainforest. They help keep it planted by eating fruit and spitting seeds about. Like a farmer putting in new crops."

Then there was screeching above us. We looked up. It looked like someone was flinging blue and yellow paint across the forest.

"Macaws," said Uncle.

"Do they spit seeds?" said Maria.

"No they eat them . . . and nuts . . . and stones . . . and soil," said Uncle.

"Yuk! You're kidding!" we said.

"I'm not," said Uncle. "They swallow the stones to grind up their food inside them and the soil gives them salts for good health."

Last night Uncle took us jungle exploring in the dark! It was scary! He says it is the best time to see wildlife. Spooky eyes were glowing at us out of the black. Strange things were tapping on our skin. I saw some feroz (ferocious) big eyes coming straight

for me! Bright red ones! Terrível (Terrible)! I thought,
Oh no! A vampire thing! I
grabbed my sister! She did a
SCREAM. So I did a
SCREAM . . . too! Then the
eyes were gone. Uncle was
laughing and saying, "Are you
frightened of a moth?!" Yes,

that's right! Those frightening big eyes belonged to
just a little insecto! And we were screaming our legs
off! Ah well, now we know one more new thing.

 I will miss being here. But I am also looking
forward to being back home in Copacabana.

Big squawks,

Maria

PS I have not met anyone who wants a game of
futebol . . . yet. Perhaps I will ask the howlers'
gang to play with me.

28 Julho

Hi pen-friend,

It's me, Maria. How are you doing? What a day! We went fishing. And nearly all fell right into the Amazon!

This morning Uncle said we would go on the river to catch our dinner. So we took our boat and fishing things and went on to the water, then sat very quietly holding our lines and listening to the screaming pia birds in the treetops. They go like this . . . "DO!-TI!-DO!-DO!-TI!-DO!" Their noise is everywhere and very ear splitting. But we have never ever seen them. Not even once! What odd birds. Noisy . . . but shy too?!

— by Uncle Jesus- he <u>has</u> seen them before!

All of a sudden Leo's line was waggling like a snake. There was something on it! "Uncle . . . Uncle!" he shouted. "A fish has got me!"

"No Leo," said Uncle "You have got it!

Remember who is doing the fishing!"

By now the fish was really jumping about.

And so was Leo!

"Stay calm Leo!" said Uncle. "And just bring it in nice and gently."

Suddenly there was a flash of silver. The fish jumped straight out of the water and into our boat. Right at Leo's feet! And Leo almost jumped straight out of the boat and into the water. Because the fish was a really dangerous piranha! It was bouncing around in the boat-bottom and snapping with its big razor teeth right near his toes. He put his legs up in the air and waved them about, shouting "Save me Uncle! Save me!" He was rocking and rolling so much that I thought our boat would tip up.

But Uncle just said, "Don't worry," and gave the piranha a hard knock with his paddle and it was dead. So that was that!

We caught quite a few more different sorts of fish (the Amazon is full of them!) and on the way back to our camp we stopped at a riverside village to buy some extra ones and also a few bananas from the Indians who lived there.

As Uncle was paying an old Indian man with some fishing hooks and matches and stuff we noticed a commotion in the jungle. It was a big gang of Indian children and teenagers all rushing around a clearing like mad things.

Leo could hardly believe his eyes! They were playing futebol! "Can I? Can I Uncle?" he cried to Uncle.

Uncle just smiled and said, "Sure Leo. Go ahead and show them your stuff!"

While Leo was galloping around the football field with the Indian children me and Uncle talked to some other ones who wanted to show us their pets. Not just cats and dogs . . . but sloths and snakes too!

A little girl asked us where we were from and when we told her she wanted to know how long it had taken us to paddle our canoe all the way from Rio to her village!

Tonight, as we sat by the campfire talking about our excitement-packed day, Uncle told us some more about piranhas. He told us a story that a farmer had once told him.

The farmer was leading his donkey across a shallow river. Just before they went in the donkey scratched its leg on a thorn. The man didn't notice. Halfway across the donkey began jumping and making terrible noises. Hundreds of piranha fish had smelled blood from its scratch. It was being attacked by them! The farmer ran out of the water fast. But the donkey stayed in. The man could not help. He just had to stand and watch it being

eaten alive! After only a minute or two there was nothing at all left of that donkey but its bones! The fish had eaten every other single part of it.

"So I did have a narrow escape today!" said Leo, when Uncle had finished. "Well no, I don't think just one piranha was a problem," said Uncle. "And anyway, many piranha stories are overdone a bit. They are not quite as bad as people think. Just every now and again something terrible does come up!"

Well, I am going to climb in my hammock now. I am worn in!

Fancy a swim before we go to sleep Leo? *No thanks sis'! L.*

With all best fishes,

Maria

PS Tomorrow we are starting back for Manaus. When we get there we are going to have one more night in the big hotel again. Hmmm . . . a hot shower. We will write you again as soon as we are back home.

12 Agosto (August)

Hi pen friend,

How do you do do? It's me, Maria. And me, Leo. We are home. Yes . . . back from the jungle at last! In crazy Copacabana once more. It is so busy mad here. So much concrete! And so many cars! But so very nice to be back. With our mum and dad again. And our sea and beach. And our pals. But maybe we are just a little bit sad. For our jungle camp by the riverside. And even all those noisy animals.

Are you busy or relaxing? For us the holiday is gone! So we are normal again. We are back to school. But it is great. We are like two famous explorers come back from their big expedition.

Worst of all has been Mr Anaconda. Yes! He has been like a man with a bee in his bottom! He just won't stop! "Did you see this?", "Did you see that?" On and on and on he goes. I think we will have to take him with us next time we have a holiday. Only joking! He has asked us each to do a special piece of work about our best most interesting Amazon adventure things for him and all the class. And for YOU. So we have. He says they are great. And here they are.

We hope you like them!

With all our best love to you!

Leo and Maria

My special Amazon holiday work – by Leo Lisboa

Oi! As you all know I have been on a great adventure to the Amazon river with my famous Uncle Jesus and my twin sis' (who is not a bit famous). So here, as my special treat for you all, is my ace writing and drawing about the most best things we saw when we came back down the river in our canoe. It is brilhante:

WHAT WE SAW ON THE AMAZON RIVER

An Anaconda (yes . . . real!) — six metres long (that's three very tall teachers end to end!). And as thick as my Uncle's middle times two. Back end in the water — head end on mud bank. We thought it was covered in flowers! But they all flew away when it moved. They were butterflies! It had seen a caiman (an alligator). There was a big lot of splashing. The snake got it and crushed it. Then swallowed it, all in one piece! _No manners, these anacondas!_

Yum Yum!

A Pirarucu Fish — being caught by Indians fishing with spears. It was massive. They have got teeth on their tongues! The Indians cut them out and make them into fruit graters. And they make their skin scales into fingernail filers!

<u>Garimpeiro</u> — a gold hunter. Not a wild animal (well, I don't think so). We had already met him on the big hammock boat (that is why he is waving). There is gold in the river mud. Garimpeiros put a poison called mercury in it  to make the gold come out. This goes into the water and kills the fish and other wildlife. What is the fuss about gold? I think a healthy rainforest is better!

<u>Candirus Fish</u> — all swimming near our canoe. They are tiny catfish. When people are in the water they sometimes swim up their noses. Or even up their bottoms! Or even more private places than that! Uuurgh! They stick in their sharp little spines so that they can stay for ever. Ouch!

<u>A Jabiru Stork</u> — catching a big frog. It hunts by feeling — not by looking. It just sticks its big bill in the water and waits until something bumps into it. Then it eats it!

<u>Giant Water Lilies</u> – like huge green dinner plates (and like my sister's carnival dress). Enorme! Nearly two metres from one side to the other.

Uncle Jesus said you could sit a baby on it and it wouldn't sink!

<u>Stingray</u> – on the river bed but camouflaged. Uncle said one once whipped its tail at him when he was wading. He was in a big pain for a whole day.

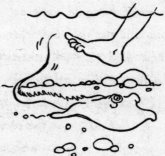

<u>A marine Toad</u> – these have got poisonous skin to stop things eating them. If they do get eaten – no problem! They just pump themselves up like a futebol inside their attacker's throat until it changes its mind . . . or chokes to death!

My special Amazon work by M. Lisboa

Since our very good lesson from Mr Anaconda and our tremendous holiday in the Amazon I am really interested in the rainforest Indians. I have been doing a lot of reading and also asking my very clever Uncle questions. I've found out loads! So here for you is. . .

THE AMAZING YANOMAMI INDIANS

Deep in the rainforest there are some Indian tribes who have not been discovered and some others who have only just been discovered. One of the tribes who have only just been found is a tribe called the Yanomami!

The Yanomami have always stayed exactly the same right up until about 25 years ago. All the time until then they were hidden away in the middle of this jungle with no wheels, no roads, no telephones, no electricity, only the forest. Living the same as they had for thousands and thousands of years. Modern people didn't know they were there and they didn't know modern people were there!

Then suddenly one day some people in aeroplanes found the Yanomami! And that was that! Modern times arrived in their life quick fast! As if someone had whizzed them forward thousands of years - but in just a few weeks!

The modern people gave them tools and stuff, but tools weren't the only things they got. Some of them got our illnesses like measles and flu which they couldn't get better from. So a lot of them died. Now people from the modern world aren't allowed to visit them in case they give them diseases. Only the people who help them and study their life are allowed to go. Uncle knows some of these people.

Here is some of the amazing stuff they have found out.

Yanomami means Human Beings. There are probably about 25,000 of them altogether. They have got about 320 villages hidden deep in the jungle.

In the village they all live in a big round house called a Yano which is made from palm-tree leaves and wooden posts. Each one of the families has its own separate part of the big house to live in. Just like we have our own separate flat in our apartment block! In their own bit they have a fire burning all the time which they put their hammocks around for sleeping.

dried palm tree leaves

wooden supports

hammock

fire (it gets a bit smokey!)

They do not write and read, they don't use the days of the week or months of the year, and they do not need to count past two - after that they just say "many"! A lot of their children don't go to school like we do to learn spelling and maths, but they are always learning about the forest and its animals and plants and how to stay alive.

They don't wear many clothes but they decorate themselves with colours which they get from forest plants. Sometimes they stick reeds under their bottom lips and thin sticks of wood through their noses.

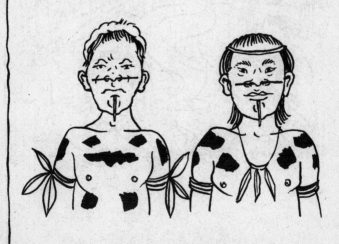

This is really amazing! When a Yanomami person dies their family and friends hang their body up from a tree until it is completely dry. Afterwards they burn the bones until they are just ashes. Then they mix the ashes up with bananas and drink them in a soup!

The End

14 Agosto

Hi pen-friend,

It's me Maria. And me Leo. And this is our very last
letter to you. So we are melancolico (sob sob!). But
also happy (hurrah hurrah!). Because we have
done what our good Uncle asked us. We have taken
you to the Amazon with us in our letters! So he is
very pleased with us. And we have loved every bit
of it.

We hope you have learned some things about
our country. And enjoyed yourself as well. We really
are sorry to leave you. Because we like you just
soooo much! But we have got to go. We have got
new work from Mr Anaconda. And soon it will be
time to start our Carnival practice once more.

And for Leo to get his futebol squad in training.

Oh yes – I forgot to tell you! Aldo is back. His family did not have to stay in Brasilia after all. So we have got our keeper again. Our net is once more safe. NO GOOOLA! NO GOOOLA! NO GOOOLA!

Now . . . we really must go. Mum and Dad send best wishes. And Uncle sends you his deepest compliments. He hopes you are well. He is very happy right now. Why? Because he got his special insecto after all. Mum found him another one, when she was unpacking Leo's washing from the holiday.

Yes! It was hiding. In Leo's sock!

Tchau! Adeus!

We love you.

Bye-bye,

Leo & Maria   XXXXXXXXXX